Go To Bed

Let's go to bed.

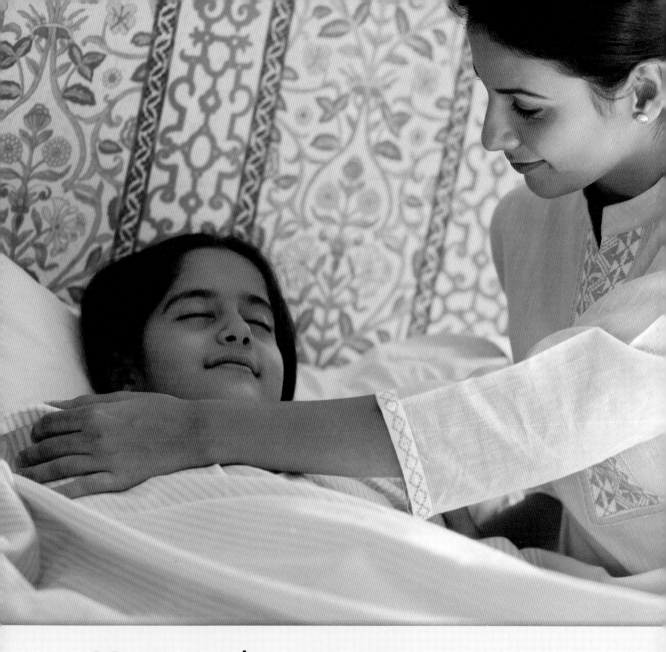

Mum tucks me up.

Rex naps on a rug.

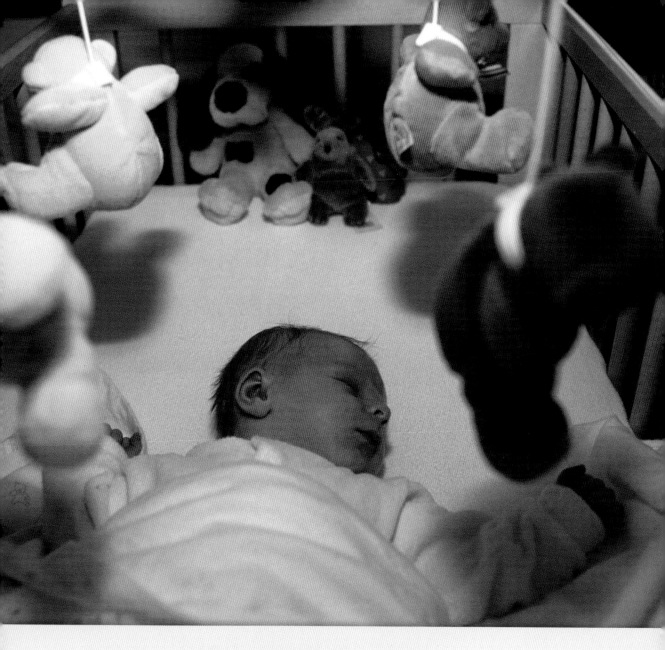

Jon naps in his cot.

The twins can swop beds.

Mum's nest has six in a bed!

Tiva's bed is in a wigwam.

I go to bed in a bag!

A bed in a box can be snug.

I go to bed on a mat.

A bed in a den is just the job.

A bed in a den can be at the top!

Mum lets Jess nap with me.

I go to bed if I am not well.

Jip has not got a bed!